What Else Can I Pl...
Piano
Grade Two

Series Editor: Mark Mumford

Music arranged and processed by
Barnes Music Engraving Ltd
East Sussex TN22 4HA, England

Published 1995

Introduction

In this *What Else Can I Play?* collection you'll find nineteen popular tunes that are both challenging and entertaining.

The pieces have been carefully selected and arranged to create ideal supplementary material for young pianists who are either working towards or have recently taken a Grade Two piano examination.

Technical demands increase progressively, gradually introducing new concepts that reflect the requirements of the major examination boards. Each piece offers suggestions and guidelines to fingering, dynamics and tempo, together with technical tips and performance notes.

Pupils will experience a wide variety of music, ranging from folk and classical through to showtunes and popular songs, leading to a greater awareness of musical styles.

Whether it's for light relief from examination preparation, or to reinforce the understanding of new concepts, this collection will enthuse and encourage all young piano players.

Johnny Todd

Traditional

This traditional tune, from Northumbria in the north of England, was adapted as the theme music for *Z Cars*, a 1960s series of television dramas about the work of the police. The Z stood for Ford Zephyrs and Zodiacs, cars commonly in use with the police at that time.

This piece has a simple melody in the right hand with an *Alberti bass* accompaniment in the left hand. Try to keep the left hand flowing smoothly Tod follow the phrase marks carefully.

Do-Re-Mi

Words by Oscar Hammerstein II, Music by Richard Rodgers

Moderato (♩ = 118)

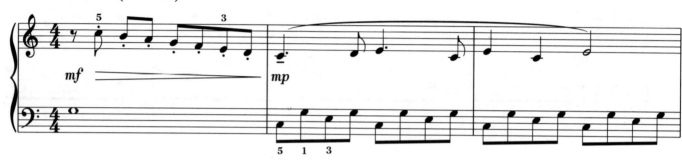

This is one of the most famous songs from Rodgers and Hammerstein's 1959 musical, *The Sound Of Music*. Do, Re and Mi are the first three notes of the major scale. This system of naming notes is called *Tonic Sol-Fa*. It was developed by Sarah Glover in the early nineteenth century and later adapted by John Curwen.

The melody in this song rises one note every other bar, gradually climbing the scale. Observing the tenuto marks ♩ will help to emphasise the beginning of each of these two bar phrases.

Moon river

Words by Johnny Mercer, Music by Henry Mancini

Moon River comes from the film *Breakfast At Tiffany's* (1961). During his lifetime Henry Mancini wrote the music to over one hundred films, including *The Pink Panther*.

Aim to play this piece as smoothly as possible – like a gently flowing river. You might consider using the pedal from time to time, for example at bars 9 and 11.

Stairway to heaven

Words and Music by Jimmy Page and Robert Plant

Slowly and expressively (♩ = 72)

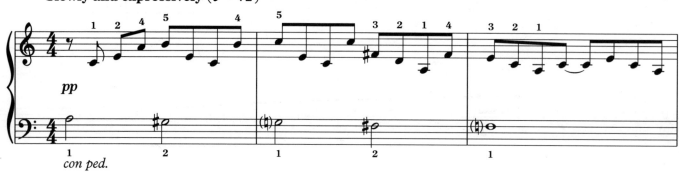

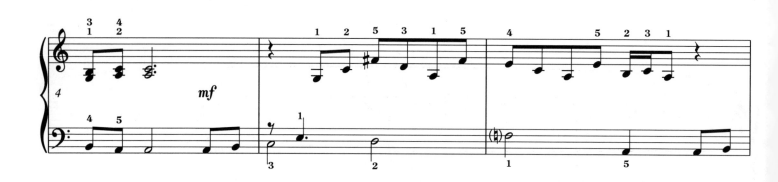

Stairway To Heaven appeared on the fourth album by the rock band *Led Zeppelin,* in 1971. The song is one of the most requested songs on American radio. In 1993 it was re-recorded and became a top ten hit for Rolf Harris, much to everyone's amazement.

Notice how the melody moves from the bass clef into the treble clef. When the melody does appear in the lower register, concentrate on giving the notes full clarity.

Sheep may safely graze

J. S. Bach

This is a well known *aria* from one of Bach's *cantatas*. A cantata is, literally, a piece to be sung. Typically, solo voices and chorus are featured, with instrumental accompaniment.

Don't be tempted to rush through this beautiful tune, especially at bars 9 to 20.

Over the rainbow

Words by E. Y. Harburg, Music by Harold Arlen

Over The Rainbow was written for the musical film *The Wizard Of Oz*, which was released in 1939 and starred the legendary singer Judy Garland.

Use a singing tone to bring out the beauty of the melodic phrases. Watch out for the change of mood in the middle section, bars 17 to 24, and its contrasting musical style. Careful use of pedal may help to bring atmosphere to this song.

Chitty Chitty Bang Bang

Words and Music by Richard M Sherman and Robert B Sherman

The 1968 film *Chitty Chitty Bang Bang* cost ten million dollars to make. The music was written by the Sherman brothers who also wrote the music for *Mary Poppins*.

Keep your wrists supple through this piece and you will find the chords at the beginning and end easier to play. If your fingers are relaxed too, the repeated G's of the melody will be easier to produce as well.

Autumn leaves

English Words by Johnny Mercer, French Words by Jacques Prevert, Music by Joseph Kosma

Slowly, with feeling (♩ = 48)

This song, of which the well known refrain or chorus is shown here, is made up of short melodic phrases. Can you see how each new phrase moves down one note of the scale? This is known as a *sequence*.

To achieve the feeling in this piece you will probably need to use *tempo rubato*. This means that you can be slightly flexible with the rhythm of the music. Variation in tempo can help to create mood in some pieces.

rall. molto

If

Words and Music by David Gates

If is a hugely popular romantic ballad, written by David Gates of the pop group *Bread*. The song was first released in 1971.

Try practising the syncopated rhythm of the melody, at bar 9, right hand separately. This pattern occurs again later in the song.

The green leaves of summer

Words by Paul Francis Webster, Music by Dmitry Tiomkin

The music for this song was written by Dmitry Tiomkin (1894–1979) who was a Russian-American composer and pianist. As well as composing many film scores Tiomkin performed the European première of George Gershwin's *Piano Concerto in F*.

The rise and fall of the short melodic phrases help to create a thoughtful mood in this piece. Paying careful attention to the dynamics will ensure an effective atmosphere.

Eastenders

By Leslie Osborne and Simon May

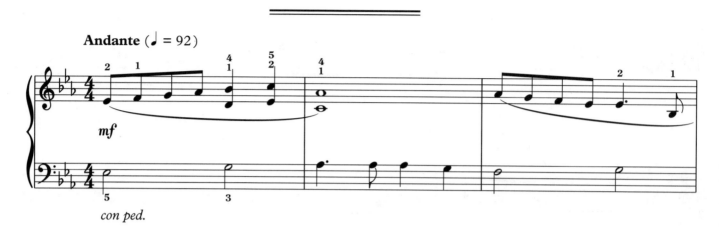

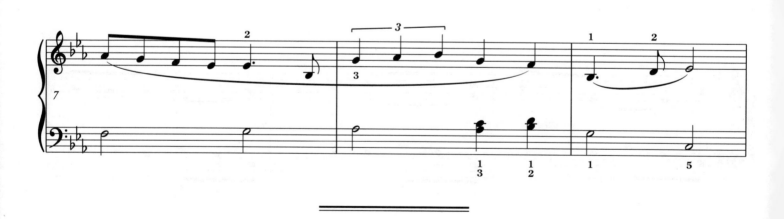

EastEnders is the BBC's most popular long-running soap opera. Although Albert Square is fictional, it is actually based on a real place – Fassett Square in Hackney, East London.

You probably know this melody quite well, but be careful! There are some tricky leaps, for instance at bar 4. Watch your fingering and keep the music as *legato* as possible.

23

Figaro's air

W. A. Mozart

This aria is taken from Mozart's *Le Nozze Di Figaro* (The Marriage Of Figaro) which is set in the Spanish city of Seville in the 17th Century. The opera was first performed in 1786.

In just twenty-four bars this piece goes through a number of mood changes. Just look at the musical elements: *legato* and *staccato*, *fortissimo* to *piano*, high register melodies and low register melodies, arpeggios and scales – at least there are no accidentals! Pay careful attention to all of these contrasts.

The ash grove

Welsh Traditional

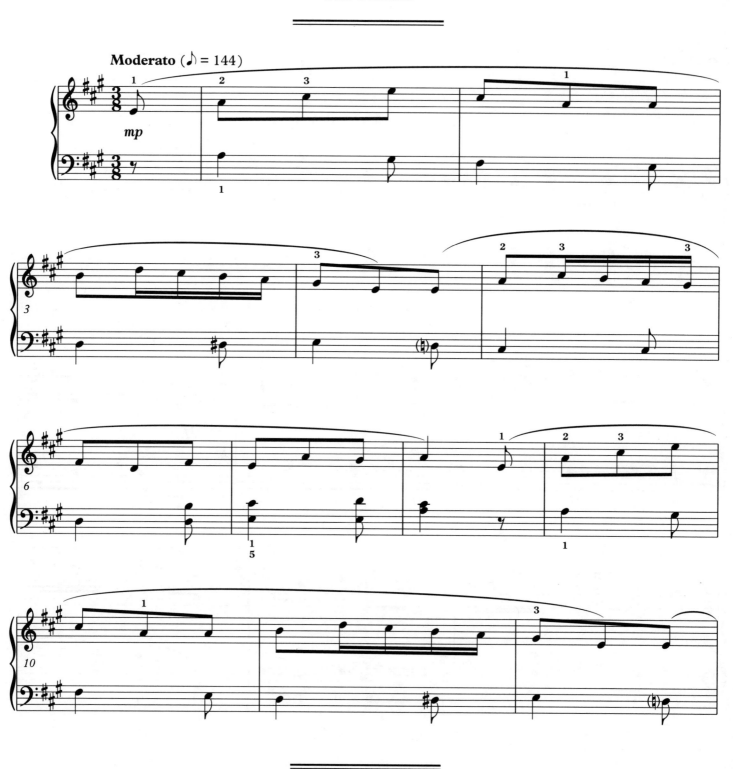

The *Ash Grove* is a traditional Welsh folk song, also known as *Llwyn On*.

Keep an even tempo. Although the time signature is 3/8 it is not at all fast. Aim for a singing style in the right hand. In instrumental music this quality is called *cantabile*.

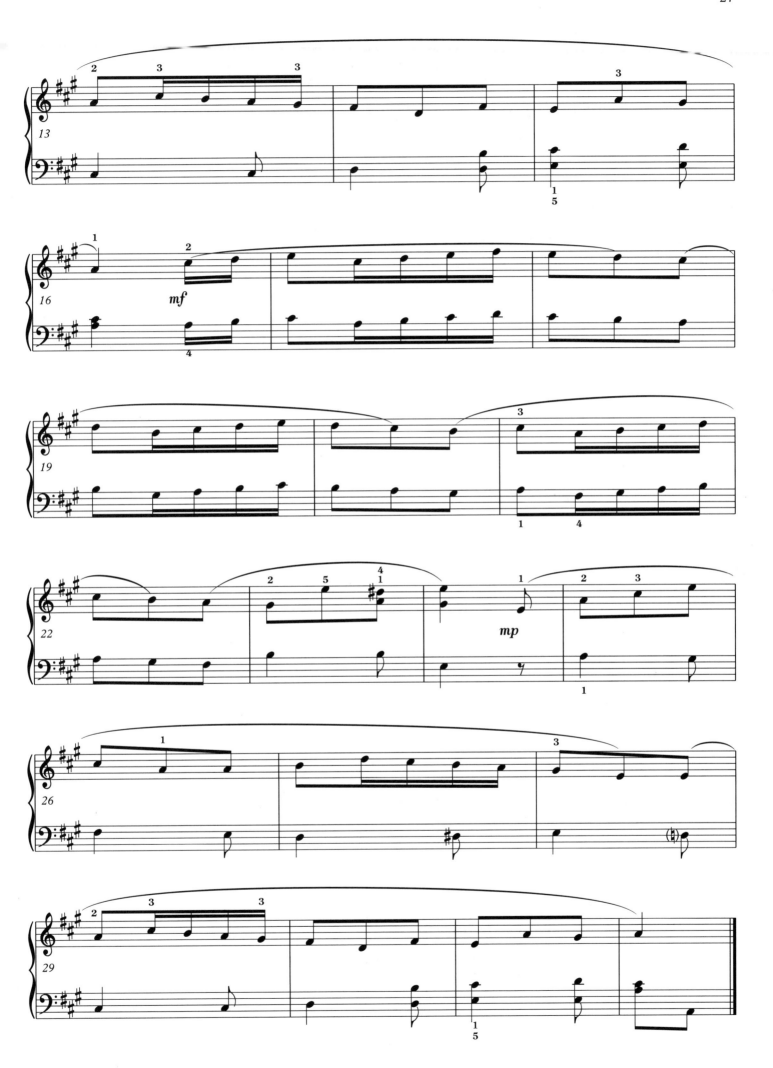

The Christmas song
(Chestnuts roasting on an open fire)

Words and Music by Mel Torme and Robert Wells

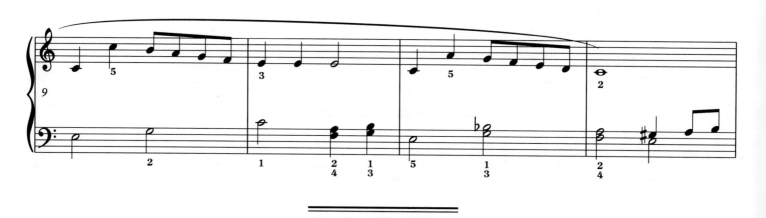

This classic Christmas song has been recorded by many artists, but Nat King Cole's version, of 1946, is probably the most memorable.

There are some unexpected shifts of harmony in this piece and this inevitably means – accidentals! Look at bars 6 to 8. Practise these parts separately, at first.

Barnacle Bill
(Theme from Blue Peter)

H. Ashworth-Hope

Not too fast (♩ = 126)

Barnacle Bill has been most famously used as the theme for *Blue Peter*, the longest running children's programme on British television. A Blue Peter is actually a flag used by ships to signal an immediate sailing.

Lots of slow practice will help to bring this number to performance standard. The sea-shanty style dictates that the quavers should run freely. However, don't rush the quaver passages.

Eine kleine nachtmusik
(minuet and trio)

W. A. Mozart

Eine Kleine Nachtmusik (A Little Night Music) is a *Serenade* of four movements and was originally written for stringed instruments. The word serenade is thought to derive from the Italian *sereno*, meaning calm, although a serenade is also considered to be music of the evening, *sera*. Traditionally sung or played as an act of courtship or courtesy, the serenade was developed by eighteenth-century composers as chamber music in several movements.

Notice that the upbeat *anacrusis* is included within each of the repeat sections.

We're off to see the wizard

Words by E. Y. Harburg, Music by Harold Arlen

Bright march (♩. = 92)

This is another song from the classic film musical *The Wizard Of Oz* (1939). Writer Harold Arlen (1905-1986) spent much time in Hollywood composing songs, including *It's Only A Paper Moon*, *Stormy Weather* and *That Old Black Magic*.

A light bouncy touch will help maintain the jaunty feel of the rhythm in this song. However, watch out for the accented chords in bars 2 and 22.

Cavatina

Music by Stanley Myers

Cavatina is the theme tune from the 1978 film *The Deer Hunter*. The most famous version was recorded by guitarist John Williams.

In this piece the right hand plays the melody *and* part of the accompaniment. Keep the melody sustained whilst letting the accompanying quavers move gently beneath.

Getting to know you

Words by Oscar Hammerstein II, Music by Richard Rodgers

This is a song from the stage musical *The King And I*, a show based on Anna Leonowen's book *The English Governess At The Siamese Court*. Gertrude Lawrence first conceived of the story as a stage musical, and played the part of Anna, opposite Yul Brynner, when the show opened in New York in 1951.

The tune is graceful and the sentiment one of warming friendship. Keep a nice even tempo and don't rush the quaver triplets. Watch out for the two-part writing in the right hand part.